It's Easy To Play Walt Disney.

Wise Publications
London/ New York/ Sydney

Exclusive distributors
Music Sales Limited
8/9 Frith Street, London W1V 5TZ, England.
Music Sales Pty. Limited
120 Rothschild Avenue, Rosebery, NSW 2018, Australia.
This book © Copyright 1980 by
Wise Publications
ISBN 0.86001.697.8
Order No. WD 10260

Compilation: Peter Evans
Arranger: Cyril Watters

Music Sales complete catalogue lists thousands
of titles and is free from your local music
book shop, or direct from Music Sales Limited.
Please send a cheque or Postal Order for £1.50 for postage to
Music Sales Limited, 8/9 Frith Street, London W1V 5TZ.

Printed in England by
Eyre & Spottiswoode Limited, London and Margate, Kent

A Spoonful Of Sugar

Words and music by
Richard M. Sherman and Robert B. Sherman

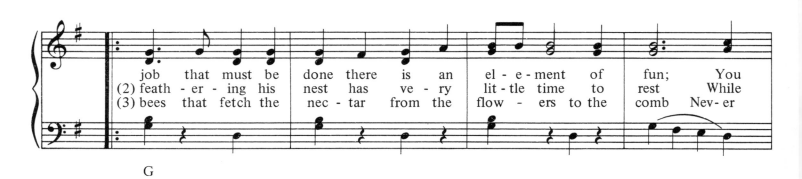

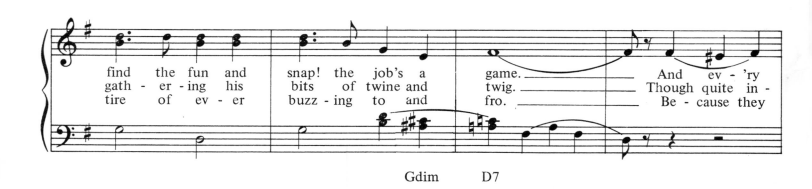

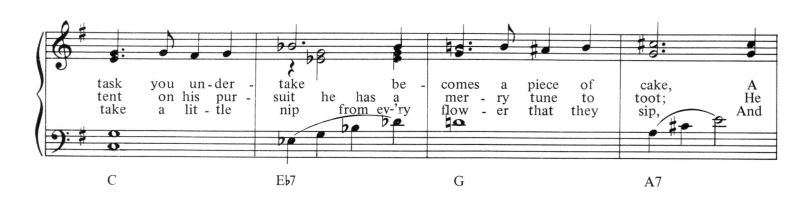

©Copyright 1963 Wonderland Music Company Incorporated.
This arrangement ©Copyright 1979 Wonderland Music Company Incorporated.
Used by Music Sales Limited, London W1 with permission.

CHORUS

The Unbirthday Song

Words and music by
Mack David, Al Hoffman and Jerry Livingston

Fairly bright

VERSE

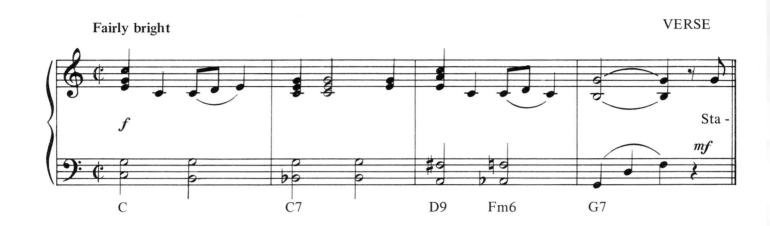

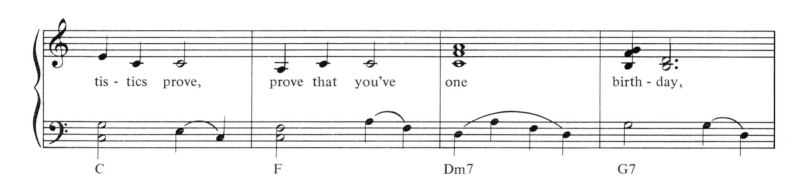

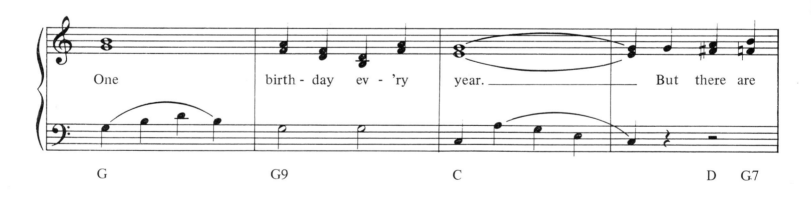

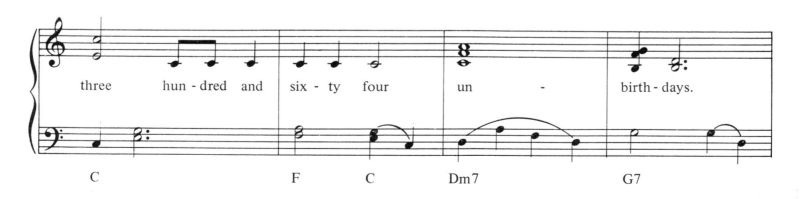

©Copyright 1948 Walt Disney Music Company.
This arrangement ©Copyright 1979 Walt Disney Music Company.
Used by Music Sales Limited, London W1 with permission.

ve - ry mer-ry un - birth-day to us, to us, A

C

ve - ry mer-ry un - birth-day to us, to us. _____ If

Cdim   Dm7   G7

there   are no ob - jec - tions, let it be u - nan - i - mous, _____ A

C   C7   Gm7 C7   Dm A Dm A7   Dm Cdim

ve - ry mer-ry un - birth-day,   a   ve - ry mer-ry un - birth-day,   a

Dm7   G7   Dm7   G7   Dm7   G7   Dm7   G7

ve - ry mer-ry un - birth-day to   all.

8 Dm7   G7   Dm7 G7 G+   C   F   C G7 C

A Dream Is A Wish Your Heart Makes

Words and music by
Mack David, Al Hoffman and Jerry Livingston

©Copyright 1948 Walt Disney Music Company.
This arrangement ©Copyright 1979 Walt Disney Music Company.
Used by Music Sales Limited, London W1 with permission.

Your rain-bow will come smil - ing through; _____

Dm   G7   G7+   C

_____ No mat - ter how your heart is griev-ing, if you keep on be -

B   C   Am   F7   D7   G   B7   Em

liev - ing the dream that you wish will come

A7   C   D   C   D9   D7♭9

1   **2**

true.   A   true.

G   Gdim   C6   D7   G   G7

rallentando

C   Cm   G

Ped.   *

Never Smile At A Crocodile

Words by Jack Lawrence
Music by Frank Churchill

©Copyright 1952 Walt Disney Music Company.
This arrangement ©Copyright 1979 Walt Disney Music Company.
Used by Music Sales Limited, London W1 with permission.

The Ugly Bug Ball

Words and music by
Richard M. Sherman and Robert B. Sherman

Once a

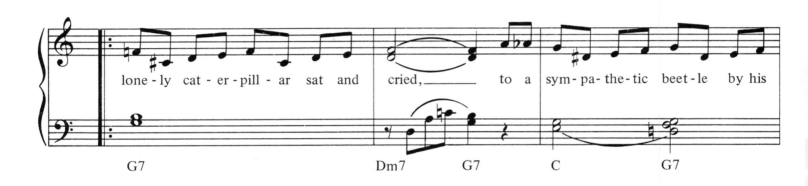

lone-ly cat-er-pill-ar sat and cried, to a sym-pa-the-tic beet-le by his

side, "I've got no-bo-dy to hug, I'm such an

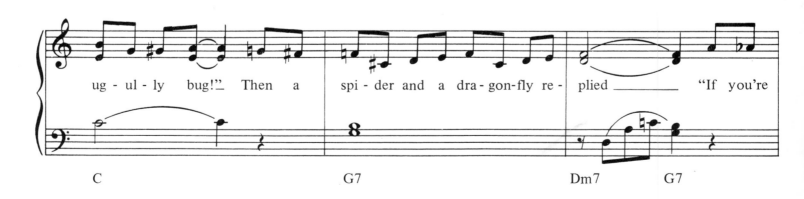

ug-ul-ly bug!" Then a spi-der and a dra-gon-fly re-plied "If you're

©Copyright 1962 Wonderland Music Company Incorporated.
This arrangement ©Copyright 1979 Wonderland Music Company Incorporated.
Used by Music Sales Limited, London W1 with permission.

se - ri - ous and want to win a bride, Come a - long_ with us

C   Em   Am   A♭7

to the glor - i - ous an - i - mal Ug - ly Bug Ball." Come on, let's

C   G7   C   C7+

crawl, got - ta crawl, got - ta crawl to the Ug - ly Bug Ball, to the ball, to the

F   C   Gm6

ball, and a hap - py time we'll have there, one and

A7   D7   G7

1   **2**

all, at the Ug - ly Bug Ball._ Once a Ball._

sfz

C7   F   C   C   C   15

You Can Fly, You Can Fly, You Can Fly

Words by Sammy Cahn
Music by Sammy Fain

Moderato

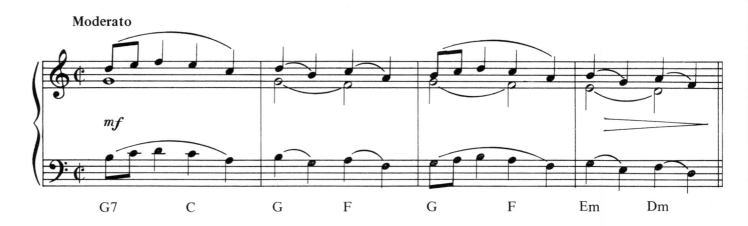

G7   C   G   F   G   F   Em   Dm

1. Think of the pres-ents you've brought; An - y mer-ry lit - tle thought.
2. Think of the happ - i - est things; That's the way to get your wings.

C   F   C

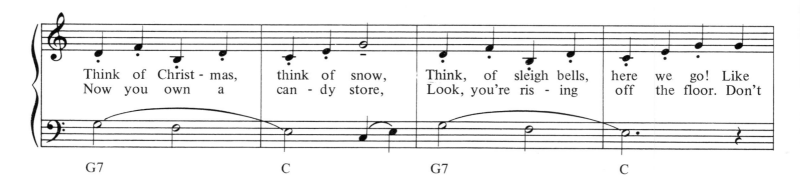

Think of Christ - mas, think of snow, Think, of sleigh bells, here we go! Like
Now you own a can - dy store, Look, you're ris - ing off the floor. Don't

G7   C   G7   C

To Coda

rein - deer in the sky,_____ You can fly! You can
won - der how or why,_____

F   Dm   G7   C

©Copyright 1951 Walt Disney Music Company.
This arrangement ©Copyright 1979 Walt Disney Music Company.
Used by Music Sales Limited, London W1 with permission.

fly! You can fly! fly! You can

fly! Soon you'll zoom all a - round the room, All it

takes is faith and trust. But the thing that's a pos - i - tive must is a

lit - tle bit of Pix - ie dust. The dust is a pos - i - tive must.

D.%. al Coda

🔴 *CODA*

fly! You can fly! You can fly!

He's A Tramp

Words and music by
Sonny Burke and Peggy Lee

©Copyright 1952 Walt Disney Music Company.
This arrangement ©Copyright 1979 Walt Disney Music Company.
Used by Music Sales Limited, London W1 with permission.

tramp, _____ he's a scoun-drel, _____ He's a roun-der, _____ he's a

C   **B♭6**   **C**   **B♭maj7**   **F**   **Cdim**

cad, _____ He's a tramp, _____ but I love him. _____ Yes,

Gm7   **Am**   **C7**   **F**

ev - en I have got it pret - ty bad. _____ You can

B♭7   **Gm7**   **C7**   **F**

nev - er tell when he'll show up; He gives you plen - ty of

Cm7   **F7**   **Cm7**   **F9**   **B♭**   **F7**

trou - ble. I guess he's just a no 'count pup, —

B♭   **G7**   **Dm**

19

But I wish that he were dou - ble, He's a tramp, _____ he's a

D7   Gm   C   B♭6

ro - ver _____ And there's no - thing _____ more to say. _____ If he's a

C   B♭maj7   F   Cdim   Gm7

1

tramp, _____ he's a good one _____ and I wish that I could tra - vel his

Am   C7   F   B♭7   Gm7   C9

2

way. _____ He's a wish that I could tra - vel his way.

F   B♭7   Gm7   C9   F

   B♭7   C7   F

The Bare Necessities

Words and music by
Terry Gilkyson

©Copyright 1964 Wonderland Music Company Incorporated.
This arrangement ©Copyright 1979 Wonderland Music Company Incorporated.
Used by Music Sales Limited, London W1 with permission.

23

Bella Notte

Words and music by
Sonny Burke and Peggy Lee

©Copyright 1952 Walt Disney Music Company.
This arrangement ©Copyright 1979 Walt Disney Music Company.
Used by Music Sales Limited, London W1 with permission.

take the love ___ of your loved one, you'll need it a - bout this

F   Dm7   Cmaj7   G+

time   To keep from fall -ing like a star, ___ when you

Cmaj7   Em   A7   Em7   A6

make that diz - zy climb.   For this ___ is the night ___ and the

Am   C   D7   D+   G

hea - vens are right ___ on this love - ly Bel - la Not - te.

Dm6   E7   Am7   D7   G   D9

1

love - ly Bel - la Not - te.   *Ritard.*

Am7   D7   G   *Ped   **   25

2

Supercalifragilisticexpialidocious

Words and music by
Richard M. Sherman and Robert B. Sherman

©Copyright 1963 Wonderland Music Company Incorporated.
This arrangement ©Copyright 1979 Wonderland Music Company Incorporated.
Used by Music Sales Limited, London W1 with permission.

I'm Late

Words by Bob Hilliard
Music by Sammy Fain

©Copyright 1949 Walt Disney Music Company.
This arrangement ©Copyright 1979 Walt Disney Music Company.
Used by Music Sales Limited, London W1 with permission.

fuz - zy ears and | whis - kers took me | too much time to | shave.   I

Em | B7 | Em   Am6 | Em

run and then I | hop, hop, hop, I | wish that I could | fly.   There's

Dm7   G7 | C | Dm7   G7 | C

dan - ger if I | dare to stop and | here's the rea - son | why, (you see) I'm

F#m7   B7 | Em | Am7   D7 | G

o - ver - due.   I'm | in a rab - bit | stew,   Can't

Cm6 | | | D7

To Coda ⊕

ev - en say good - | bye, Hel - lo, I'm | late, I'm late, I'm | late.   {1. Good
{2. I'm

30   C | G7 | C   F | C

INTERLUDE

morn-ing Mis-ter Chat-ter-box. I'd love to stop and chat-ter, but in
off to see the Queen of Hearts who lives up in the pal-ace, and the

C   G7   C

six and sev-en-eighth min-utes I must meet with the Mad Hat-ter. The
ve-ry mo-ment I'm through with her I've got a date with Al-ice. I

A7   Dm   G7   Dm   G   C
(Melody)

mad, mad, mad, mad, Hat-ter.___ We must chat a-bout a
can't be late for Al-ice.___ Or the Queen of Hearts who

Dm   G7   C   Dm

1   **2**
D.%. al Coda

very im-por-tant mat-ter.___ I'm ___ I'm
lives up in the pal-ace.___

G7   C   Dm7   C   C

⊕ CODA

late, I'm late, I'm late.___

C   Dm7   C

31

I Wanna Be Like You

Words and music by
Richard M. Sherman and Robert B. Sherman

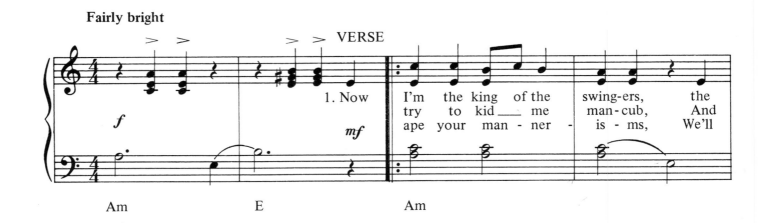

©Copyright 1966 Wonderland Music Company Incorporated.
This arrangement ©Copyright 1979 Wonderland Music Company Incorporated.
Used by Music Sales Limited, London W1 with permission.

CHORUS

tired of mon-key - in' 'round.
make my dream come true!
learn some 'et - ti - keet'!
Oh Ooh, ooh, oh! (Ee - ee) I wan-na be like

Am   G7   C

you, ooh, ooh! (Ee - ee) I wan-na walk like you, talk like you,

A7   D7   G7

too ooh, ooh. (Ee - ee) You'll see it's true, ooh, ooh! (Ee - ee) An ape like

C   Cdim   Dm   G7   C

me, ee, ee (ooh - ooh) Can learn to be Hu - ooh - ooh-man,

A7   D7   G7

1-2   3

too, Ooh ooh. (Ee - ee)   2. Don't   too, Ooh ooh. (Ee - ee)
                           3. I'll

C   E7   C   Ped

33

Little April Shower

Words by Larry Morey
Music by Frank Churchill

©Copyright 1942 Walt Disney Productions
Reproduced by permission of Campbell, Connelly & Co. Limited.

you say "Good-bye" right a - way.____ Drip, drip, drop, lit -tle Ap-ril show-er,

E   B   G7   C   G7   C   F

beat-ing a tune ev -'ry - where that you fall. Drip, drip, drop, lit -tle Ap-ril show-er,

C   F   C   Dm   C   Dm   C   G7   C   F

I'm get-ting wet and I don't care at all. Drip! Drop! Drip! Drop!

C   F   C   Dm   C   Dm   C   F   C   F

I'll nev-er be a - fraid of a good lit -tle, gay lit -tle Ap-ril ser - e -

C   F   C   Am   Dm7   G7

1

nade.____

C

2

nade.____

C   F   C   35

Bibbidi Bobbidi Boo

Words by Jerry Livingston
Music by Mack David and Al Hoffman

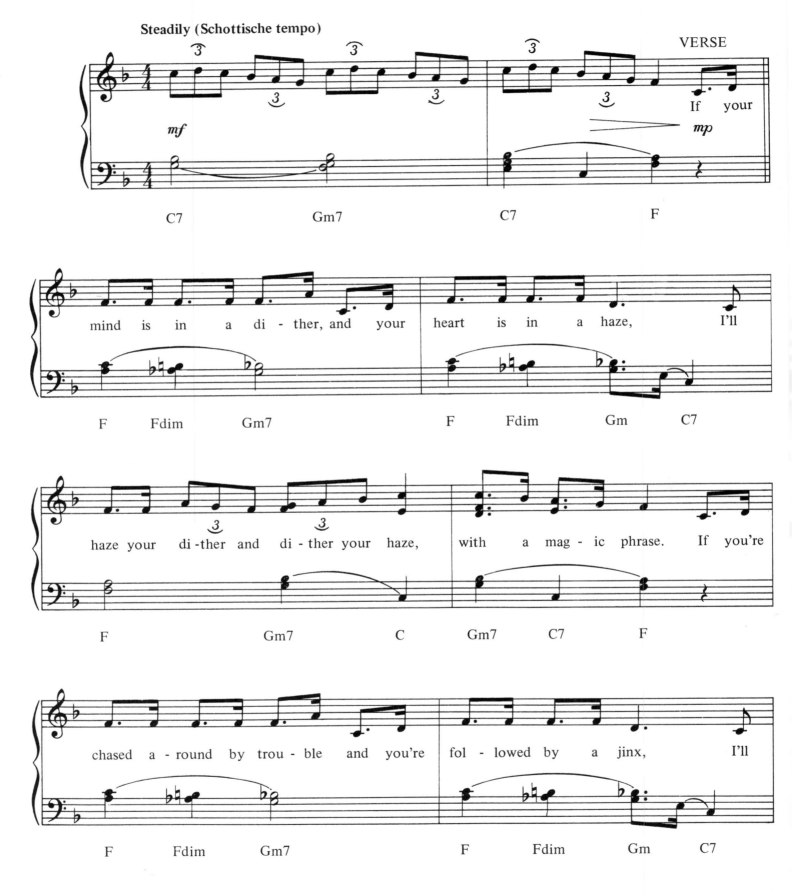

©Copyright 1948 Walt Disney Music Company.
This arrangement ©Copyright 1979 Walt Disney Music Company.
Used by Music Sales Limited, London W1 with permission.

Sa - la - ga -doo - la means   men-chic - ka -boo - le -roo,   But the

thing-a - ma - bob that does the job   is   Bib - bi - di - Bob-bi - di -Boo.

Bb   F

Dm7   G7   C7   Gm7   C7

Sa - la - ga -doo - la   men-chic - ka - boo - la   Bib - bi - di - Bob-bi - di -Boo.

F

1

Put 'em to - ge -ther and what have   you got?   Bib - bi - di - Bob-bi - di -Boo.

Gm7   C7   F

2

Bib - bi - di - Bob-bi - di - Bib - bi - di - Bob-bi - di -   Bib - bi - di - Bob-bi - di -Boo.   *sfz*

38   C7   Gm7   C7   F

Ev'rybody Wants To Be A Cat

Words by Floyd Huddleston
Music by Al Rinker

©Copyright 1968 Walt Disney Music Company.
This arrangement ©Copyright 1979 Walt Disney Music Company.
Used by Music Sales Limited, London W1 with permission.

INTERLUDE

Chim Chim Cher-ee

Words and music by
Richard M. Sherman and Robert B. Sherman

©Copyright 1963 Wonderland Music Company Incorporated.
This arrangement ©Copyright 1979 Wonderland Music Company Incorporated.
Used by Music Sales Limited, London W1 with permission.

Fortuosity

Words and music by
Richard M. Sherman and Robert B. Sherman

©Copyright 1966 Wonderland Music Company Incorporated.
This arrangement ©Copyright 1979 Wonderland Music Company Incorporated.
Used by Music Sales Limited, London W1 with permission.

The Beatles   Enya

 Phil Collins   Van Morrison   Bob Dylan

 Sting   Paul Simon   Tracy Chapman

 Eric Clapton   Pink Floyd   New Kids On The Block

 Bryan Adams   Tina Turner   Elton John

  Bee Gees  Whitney Houston   AC/DC

Bringing you the words

All the latest in rock and pop. Plus the brightest and best in West End show scores. Music books for every instrument under the sun. And exciting new teach-yourself ideas like "Let's Play Keyboard" - in cassette/book packs, or on video. Available from all good music shops.

and music

Music Sales' complete catalogue lists thousands of titles and is available free from your local music shop, or direct from Music Sales Limited. Please send a cheque or postal order for £1.50 (for postage) to:

Music Sales Limited
Newmarket Road,
Bury St Edmunds,
Suffolk IP33 3YB

 Buddy  Five Guys Named Moe  Les Misérables  West Side Story

 Phantom Of The Opera 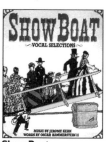 Show Boat  The Rocky Horror Show

Bringing you the world's best music.